Pets

Book Two
Revised Edition

Christian Liberty Press
Arlington Heights, Illinois 60004

A publication of
Christian Liberty Press
502 West Euclid Avenue
Arlington Heights, Illinois 60004
www.christianlibertypress.com

PALS AND PETS
    1. Phonics–Juvenile literature
    2. Reading–Juvenile literature
Written by
    Florence M. Lindstrom
Copyediting by
    Belit M. Shewan
    Edward J. Shewan
Cover Design by
    Eric D. Bristley
Illustrations by
    Vic Lockman
Colorization of Illustrations by
    Christopher D. Kou
Graphics and layout by
    Eric D. Bristley
    Christopher D. Kou
    Edward J. Shewan

ISBN 1-930092-28-8

Printed in the United States of America

Contents

Lesson 1

O o olive

Practice sounding these words, listening for the short vowel sound. Say them until you know them.

pot	pond	bug
cot	on	dug
got	Don	hug
hot		jug
not	back	mug
dot	jack	tug
lot	peck	rug
	neck	

See the pond.
The duck is on the pond.
Can Jill see the duck?
Jill can see the duck on the pond.
Tim can see a bug.

See the Duck

Jill and Tim see a duck.
It is on the pond.
It can swim and quack on the pond.
The duck got a big fish.
It got a black bug, too.

The duck is not hot.
See it go up on the mud.
It will not run fast.
It will peck at a plant.

Tim and Jill see the duck go
back to the pond and swim.
It is fun to see the duck God made.

Lesson 2

O o olive

Practice sounding these words, listening for the short vowel sound. Say them until you know them.

doll	pot	hand
	dot	and
lap	Dot	band
nap	got	sand
cap	hot	land

Jill has a doll.
The doll is Dot.
Jan has the cap for Dot.
Jill will hug Dot.
Jill is a pal for Jan.

Fun With a Doll

Jill has a doll.
The doll is Dot.
Dot can sit on Jill's lap.
It has had a nap.
It is fun to hug the doll.

Jan can see Jill and Dot.
She has a cap for Dot.
Jan will hand the cap to Jill.
Jill will fix the cap on Dot.
She is a pal for Jan.
Jan is glad for Jill.

Lesson 3

O o olive

Practice sounding these words, listening for the short vowel sound. Say them until you know them.

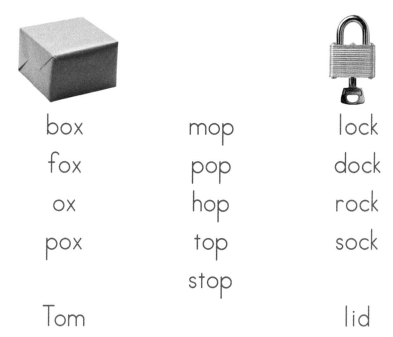

box	mop	lock
fox	pop	dock
ox	hop	rock
pox	top	sock
	stop	
Tom		lid

Tom has a box.
The lid has a lock.
Tom will lift the lock.
The lid will pop up.

bärk   The pup will bark and run.

Tom and His Pup

Tom has a pup.
It will bark and go to Tom.
It will see the box Tom has.
The box has a lock.
Tom will lift the lock.
The lid will go up.

Pop! The lid is up.
See the jack-in-the-box.
The pup can see it, too.
The pup is not glad.
It made the pup jump.
See the pup bark and run.

Lesson 4

O o   olive

Practice sounding these words, listening for the short vowel sound. Say them until you know them.

top	tent	sick
hop	went	Dick
mop	bent	lick
pop	dent	pick
stop		wick

	in	
hum	win	bud
gum	sin	mud

you

You

You can hop and run.

Tom can see you.

You can see Tom.

Can you see the top?

The Top

See the top, Tom.
It is a big top.
It can spin fast and hum.

You can run it, Tom.
You can see it go.
It is fun to see it go.

See the top go fast, Dan.
It went in the mud and will not hum.
I must pick it up fast.

I will pick up the top, Tom.
I will rub the mud, and it will spin.

O o olive

Practice sounding these words, listening for the short vowel sound. Say them until you know them.

cob	bed	rest
Bob	red	nest
rob	led	test
sob	fed	best

his	have	read

Sam will see Bob.
Bob is a pal.
Bob is glad to see Sam and Jan.
Bob got sick.
The box is for Bob.
Bob is glad to have the box.

A Gift for Bob

Dan has got a box.
The box is a gift for Bob.
Bob is sick and must not run.

He can sit up in his bed.
He can sit up and read.
He must sit still and rest.

Bob is glad to see his pals.
He sits up to see his gift.
Bob can see a top and cap in the box.
The pals will have fun.
Bob is glad for Dan and Jan.

Lesson 6

O o olive

Practice sounding these words, listening for the short vowel sound. Say them until you know them.

lock	bug	pump
rock	bugs	jump
dock	hug	hump
mock	hugs	lump
sock	jug	bump
clock	jugs	stump

Ann can see the bugs.
God made a lot of bugs.
A bug can go fast.
The bug is on the rock.
The bug is red and black.

Ann Sees a Bug

Sam and Ann sit and read.
Ann can see the bugs.
God made the bugs.
God made a lot of bugs.

Ann can see a red bug on a rock.
It will not hop and jump,
but it can go fast.
God made the bug to help us.

See the bug go on you, Ann.
You can lift the bug.
The bug must go fast.
It will go on top of the plant.

Lesson 7

E e egg

Practice sounding these words, listening for the short vowel sound. Say them until you know them.

bell	hand	bed
tell	and	red
Nell	band	
well	land	must
	sand	dust
pen		
hen	print	tap
den		lap
men	father	nap

loves

Ron loves his mother and father.

A Gift for Mother

Ron sits at his desk and taps.
His father will help him.
He must not hit his hand.
He will fix a gift for his mother.

Ron will not tell his mother yet.
He has a pen and a tag.
He will print on the tag.
The gift will be a red box for a plant.

His mother loves and helps him.
He is glad to give his mother a gift.
He loves his mother and father.

Lesson 8

E e

egg

Practice sounding these words, listening for the short vowel sound. Say them until you know them.

grass	went	hen
lass	sent	men
bass	tent	den
pass	bent	pen

from (u)   love (u)   of (uv)

they (ā)   obey (ā)
They obey God.
We will obey God.

Can you see a lion?
I can see a lion.

A Man in a Den

Nell and Ben sit on the grass.
They will read of a man in a den.
The man did not obey bad men.
He did love and obey God.

The man had to be in a den.
The den had big lions in it.
God did not let the lions kill him.
The man got help from God.
He went from the den.

God will help Nell and Ben.
He will help us, too.
We must love and obey God.

Lesson 9

E e

egg

Practice sounding these words, listening for the short vowel sound. Say them until you know them.

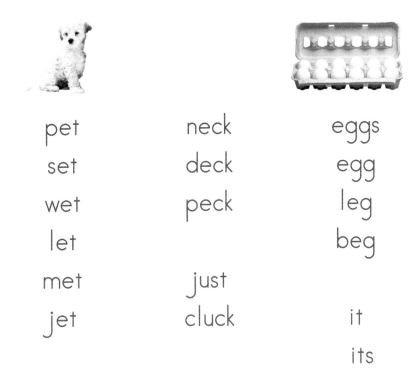

pet	neck	eggs
set	deck	egg
wet	peck	leg
let		beg
met	just	
jet	cluck	it
		its

Can you see the nest?
The nest has eggs in it.
Jed will not get the eggs.

The Pet Hen

Jed has a red hen.
He has just fed the hen.
See it peck and peck.
The hen will go to its nest.

Jed can see the hen on its nest.
He will lift the red hen.
The hen has eggs in the nest.
It will let Jed get the eggs.

Mother will fix the eggs for him.
Jed has fed his hen.
His hen has fed him.
He is glad God made his pet hen.

Lesson 10

E e

egg

Practice sounding these words, listening for the short vowel sound. Say them until you know them.

bell	sing	nest
tell	ring	rest
sell	wing	best
fell	bring	test
hell	swing	west
well	sling	pest

The bell will ring.
We will sing.
The men did the work.
The men must rest, too.

Men at Work

See the men, Dan.
I am glad the men will work.
I will be glad to go in.

The bell will tell us to go in.
We will go in and sing.
We will tell God we love Him.

We must go to Mother, Dan.
We must help Mother work.
We will tell Mother and Father that the
men did the work.

Lesson 11

E e

egg

Practice sounding these words, listening for the short vowel sound. Say them until you know them.

jet	with	bed
let		fed
wet	net	red
set	next	led
get	nest	Ted

The box is on the bed.
The box is off of the bed.
Bob has a red jet with him.
He has the red jet on his bed.
Bob is on the bed next to his jet.

The Red Jet

Bob is well and can get up.
He got up from his bed.
His mother lets him go to see Dan.
He will go with his red jet.

Dan is glad to see Bob.
Dan and Bob went next to the tent.
Bob let Dan have his jet.
Dan set the red jet on the grass.
The jet went fast on the grass.
It went to the tent.

Bob had to get the jet for Dan.
He did not let the jet hit the tent.

E e egg

Practice sounding these words, listening for the short vowel sound. Say them until you know them.

sick	tent	pill
quick	went	still
tick	bent	fill
pick	dent	will
lick	sent	hill

Pastor Tim will tell of God.

they (ā) They obey.
obey (ā) They will obey God.

stand We stand and sing.
Bible We love to read the Bible.

Dan and Jan Go

The men did the work well.
Mother and Father went in with
Dan and Ann.

It is ten, and the bell did ring.
Quick, Jan, we must go in too.

They will sit still as Pastor Tim
reads the Bible.

They will stand and sing of God.
Dan and Jan will sing for God.

They love to read the Bible.
The Bible tells of God.
It will help us obey God.

Lesson 13

E e egg

Practice sounding these words, listening for the short vowel sound. Say them until you know them.

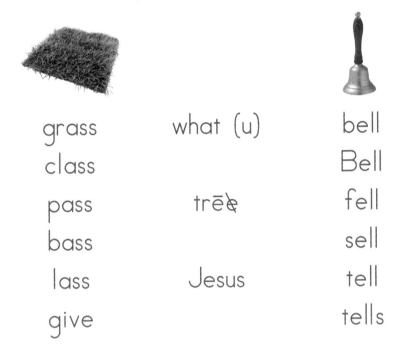

grass	what (u)	bell
class		Bell
pass	treē	fell
bass		sell
lass	Jesus	tell
give		tells

Jesus is the Son of God.
Jesus can see the man.
Miss Bell will tell the class.
The man went up in a tree.
What will he give?
He will give what he did rob.

Miss Bell and the Class

Sam and Jan sit still in the class.
Miss Bell will tell the class of a bad man.

He is not a big man.
He went up in a tree to see Jesus.

Jesus will pass the tree.
He will see the man up in the tree.
He will tell the man to go with him.

The man is glad to see Jesus, class.
He will love Jesus and not be bad.
He will give back what he did rob.
The man will obey Jesus.

Lesson 14

E e

egg

Practice sounding these words, listening for the short vowel sound. Say them until you know them.

rest	come	clock
best	some	dock
jest		block
nest		flock
pest	sōōn	lock
bless	moon	rock
bless<u>ed</u> (t)		sock

Is it time to sleep?
It soon is time to sleep.
The clock will ring six times.
What time will Ben come?
Ben will come soon.

Time to Rest

When the clock rings six
   it is time to get fed.
Mother tells me to come in
   and I will soon jump into bed.

I must pick up my socks,
   my blocks and all my mess.
When I obey my dad and mom
   God will bless and bless.

When I am snug in my bed
   and think how God has blessed,
I am glad that when I sleep
   God will not rest.